Peter Lancett is a writer, editor and film maker. He has written many books, and has just made a feature film, *The Xlitherman*.

Peter now lives in New Zealand and California.

Dark Man

Change in the Dark
by Peter Lancett
illustrated by Jan Pedroietta

Published by Ransom Publishing Ltd.
Radley House, 8 St. Cross Road, Winchester, Hampshire
SO23 9HX
www.ransom.co.uk

ISBN   978 184167 984 6

First published in 2010

Copyright © 2010 Ransom Publishing Ltd.

Dark Man

Change
in the Dark

A
play

by Peter Lancett

illustrated by Jan Pedroietta

Rans☀m

Change in the Dark
The Players

 The Dark Man
(328 words)

 The girl
(246 words)

 Narrator
(58 words)

 A boy
(10 words)

Change in the Dark
The Acts

Act One:
To the Black Water

Narrator:
> The Dark Man and the girl are in the bad part of the city.

The girl:
> I'm glad you found me. This place is scary.

The Dark Man:
> You were safe. I was watching you.

The girl:
It feels like the shadows are alive here.

The Dark Man:
Only when the Shadow Masters control them.

The girl:
    Even now, it feels like
    we're being watched.

The Dark Man:
    The Shadow Masters
    watch us. That's why we
    must hurry.

Narrator:
The Dark Man and the girl are in a black tunnel.

The girl:
Where are we going?

The Dark Man:
To the Black Water. The Old Man wants you to take power from it.

The girl:
> I hear the Black Water can make people go mad.

The Dark Man:
> The Old Man says you will be safe. You have a special gift.

Narrator:
A dog walks across their path.

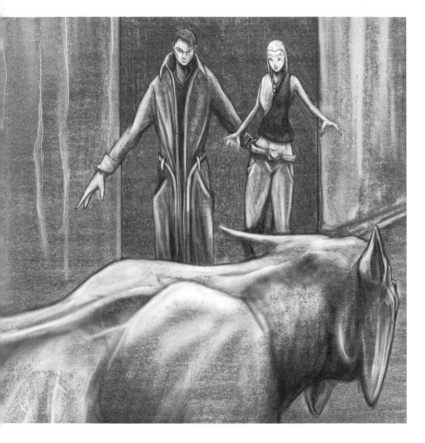

 The Dark Man:
Watch out! That dog might be a demon.

The girl:
How can you tell?

The Dark Man:
I can't. But the Shadow Masters can make demons look like animals.

The girl:
What shall we do?

The Dark Man:
Stand still.

The girl:
> Thank goodness! It's just a dog. I feel silly for being scared.

The Dark Man:
> Don't feel silly. It is good to be careful.

The girl:
>Are we near the Black Water yet? This is all so creepy.

The Dark Man:
>Not far. Come on. We must get moving.

Narrator:
>They walk on.

The girl:
So this is it. Why have we stopped?

The Dark Man:
I can't go any nearer. It's not safe for me to look at it.

The girl:
I don't feel scared. But how do I take power from it?

The Dark Man:
The Old Man says you must put your hands into the water.

Narrator:
> The girl puts her hands in the water.

The girl:
> This feels odd. Cold, running up my arms.

The Dark Man:
> The Old Man says that the water will change you.

The girl:
> I *am* changing. Look!

The Dark Man:
> I can't look. The Black Water will make me mad!

2 Act Two:
Changed

Narrator:
It is later …

A boy:
Hey, what are you doing here? This is our turf!

The girl:
Back off! If you want to live through the night.

The Dark Man:
Take it easy. We still have work to do.

The girl:
The Black Water has made me strong.

The girl:
Did you see how they ran away?

The Dark Man:
You're still changing. You must take care with your new power.

The girl:
I feel different. Do I look different?

The Dark Man:
You look darker. Now let's go.

Narrator:
The girl tries her new power.

The girl:
Wow! I love this new power. Watch what I can do!

The Dark Man:
You can freeze time, yes. But this power is not a toy.

The girl:
Chill out. This is fun!

The Dark Man:
It's not for fun. The Old Man needs you to use the power for good.

The girl:
>See this? I can take what I want.

The Dark Man:
>Put it back. That is what the Shadow Masters do.

The girl:
>What use is power if you can't have what you want?

The Dark Man:
>I think it's time we got off the streets. There's a flat nearby.

3 Act Three:
The Power to Help

Narrator:
Now they are safe in the flat.

The girl:
That was fun back there. When can we go out again?

The Dark Man:
Not until the Old Man has been to talk to you. You've changed.

The girl:
Yes, I'm stronger. And not afraid anymore.

The Dark Man:
And you need time to get used to that. Or you might hurt people.

The girl:
> Hurt people? What is happening to me? Am I turning into a monster?

The Dark Man:
> No, not a monster. But you're no longer the girl you used to be.

The girl:
> I wish I'd never seen that Black Water.

The Dark Man:
> Don't say that. You have changed, but now you have the power to help people.

The girl:
> How? I don't even know what I am anymore.

The Dark Man:
> The Old Man will help you, have no fear.

The girl:
> That's easy for you to say. You don't know what it's like!

The Dark Man:
> I know more than I can tell you. And this change is a good thing.

The girl:
> Have you been through a change yourself then?

The Dark Man:
> I was a different man, yes. A long time ago.

The girl:
> Did the Old Man use magic to change you?

The Dark Man:

He let me become the man I needed to be.

A man who can live in the dark.

A man who can fight the Shadow Masters ...

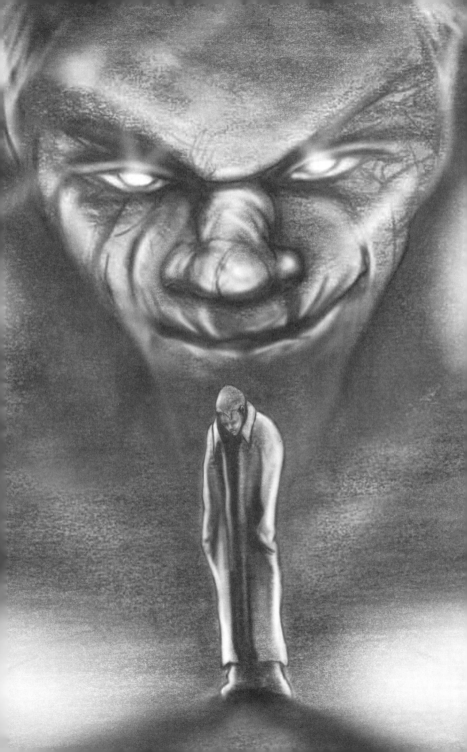

More **Dark Man** books:

Stories

Plays